Gg Hh Ii Jj Kk Ll Mm

Uu Vv Ww Xx Yy Zz

Dear Parent,

The My First Steps to Reading® *series is based on a teaching activity that helps children learn to recognize letters and their sounds. The use of predictable language patterns and repetition of familiar words will also help your child build a basic sight vocabulary. Your child will enjoy watching the characters in the books place imaginative objects in "letter boxes." You and your child can even create and fill your own letter box, using stuffed animals, cut-out pictures, or other objects beginning with the same letter. The things you can do together are limited only by your imagination. Learning letters will be fun—the first important step on the road to reading.*

The Editors

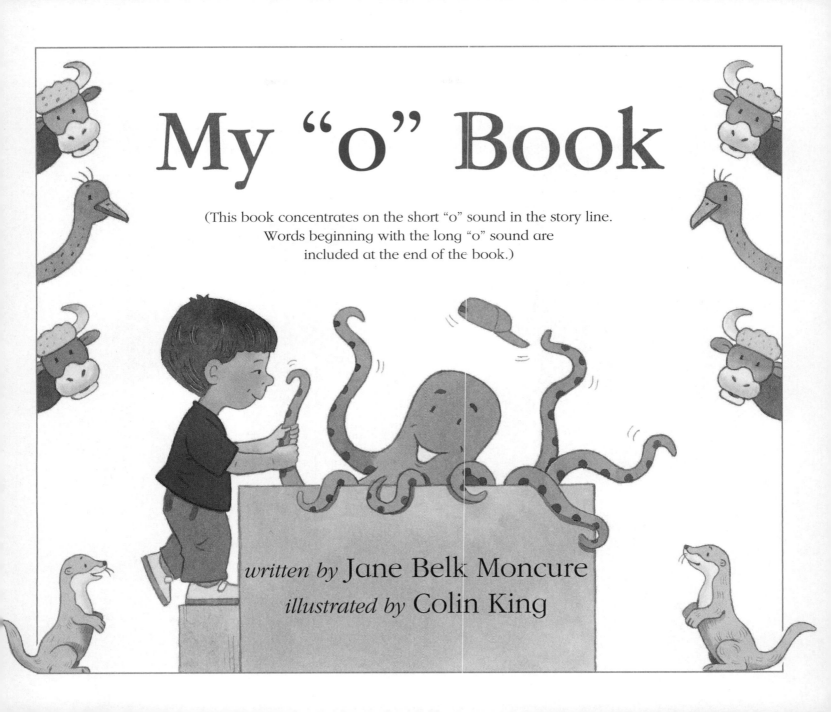

My "o" Book

(This book concentrates on the short "o" sound in the story line.
Words beginning with the long "o" sound are
included at the end of the book.)

written by Jane Belk Moncure

illustrated by Colin King

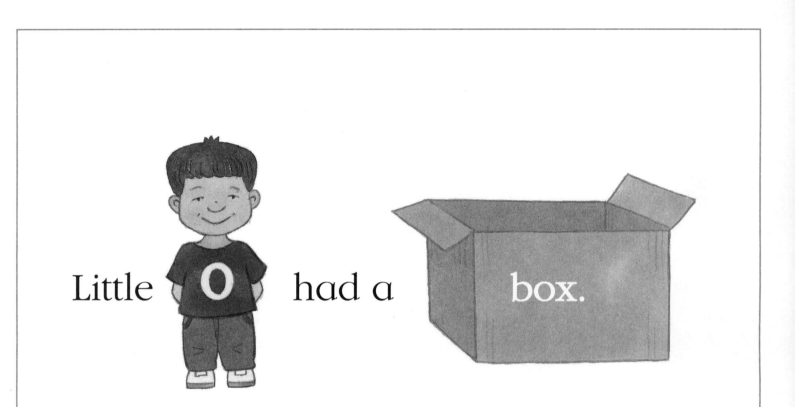

Little O had a box.

"I will find things that begin
with my 'o' sound," he said.

"I will put them into my sound box."

Little O hopped away,

hop, hop, hop.

He found otters in a pond.

Did he put the otters into his box?

He did.

Little found an octopus.

Did he put the octopus into the box with the otters? He did.

But the otters did not like the octopus.

The otters hopped out of the box,

hop, hop, hop.

Little  put a top on the box so the octopus could not get out.

Then he put the otters on top
of the box.

Away he went, hop, hop, hop.

Then Little  O found an

ostrich.

He hopped onto the ostrich.

"Hop," he said.

But the ostrich would not hop.

So Little  put the ostrich on top of the box.

Now the box was too heavy.

Little  found an OX.

"You are just what I need for my box," he said.

Away they went,
  hop,
    hop,
      hop . . .

all the way home.

Little O took his things out of the box.

ox

octopus

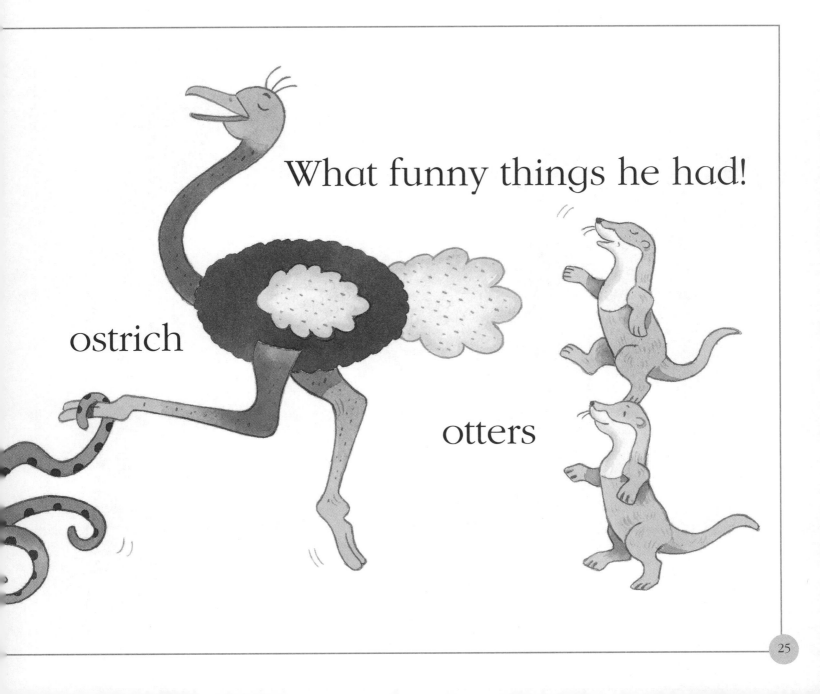

What funny things he had!

ostrich

otters

Can you read these words with Little  ?

October

S M T W T F S
1 2 3 4 5 6 7
8 9 10 11 12 13 14
15 16 17 18 19 20 21
22 23 24 25 26 27 28
29 30 31

olives

operator

ocelot

Little  has another sound in some words. He says his name, "o."

Can you read these words? Listen for Little o's name.

oatmeal

opal

ocean

My First
Steps to
READING®